Seagull is clever

Story by Beverley Randell

Illustrated by Ernest Papps

EAGLEVIEW ELEMENTARY
SUMMIT GROVE PARKWAY
THORNTON, CO 80241-1557

2

Seagull is a big bird.

He is hungry.

He is looking for fish.

Will Seagull get a fish?

No, not today.

He will not get a fish today.

The waves are too big.

Where is Seagull going?

He is going to get a shellfish.

Is Seagull eating the shellfish?

No, he is not.

Up goes Seagull
with the shellfish.
He goes up and up and up.

Down comes the shellfish!

Down,

down,

down,

down!

Seagull comes down, too.
He looks at the shellfish.
Good!
The shell is broken.

Seagull is eating the shellfish.
He is a **clever** bird.